THE SWISS FAMILY Robinson

Johann Wyss'

THE SWISS FAMILY Robinson

Adapted and Abridged by FELIX SUTTON

Illustrated by WILLIAM BARSS

GROSSET & DUNLAP · Publishers · NEW YORK

ISBN: 0-448-02136-6 (Trade Edition)

© 1960, by Grosset & Dunlap, Inc.

1975 Printing

Shipwrecked and Alone

FOR SIX DAYS our ship had battled a raging storm. The wind and lashing rain had increased their relentless fury until, by the seventh day, all hope for us was lost. We had been blown completely off our course, and the captain had no idea what part of the ocean we might be in. The crew had lost heart and were utterly exhausted.

The ship was an almost total wreck and was just barely floating. Both masts were gone. Leaks had sprung in every part of the hull. The deck slanted under our feet as water sloshed about in the flooded hold.

My heart sank as I stood in our cabin on that last night and looked at my frightened family. My four young sons — Fritz, fifteen, Ernest, thirteen, Jack, ten, and Franz, seven — were terrified. My dear wife was doing her best to cheer them up and encourage them, but it seemed like a hopeless task.

Then out of the darkness and the roar of the thundering waves, I heard the cry on deck of "Land! Land ho!" At the same instant the ship struck with a frightful shock that threw everyone to the deck. Then the timbers began to grind and groan horribly as the ship commenced to break up on the rocks.

Above the noise and din, I heard the voice of the captain:

"Lower away the boats!"

"Take courage, boys," I said. "Land is not far off and we can doubtless reach it in the lifeboats."

I quickly left them and went out on deck. But there, to my horror, I saw the last remaining boat leaving. The last seaman jumped into her and shoved off, paying no attention to my cries and pleas that they wait long enough to take us with them. My voice was drowned in the howling of the wind.

Looking frantically around in despair, I gradually became aware that our position was not completely hopeless. The stern of the ship was jammed tightly between two high rocks and was partly raised above the foaming breakers. Through the clouds of rain and mist, I could make out a line of rocky coast. My spirits lifted and my courage returned.

I returned to our cabin and made myself smile as I said:

"Things are not as bad as they seem, boys. Our ship is wrecked and will never sail again. But the rocks are holding our cabin safely above water and, if the storm lets up, we will be able to make land by tomorrow."

"Tomorrow, then," said my good wife, "we will need all our strength. We must find some food and I will make us a good supper."

Fritz and I went in search of the ship's stores, and after a good hot meal which my wife then cooked, the boys were soon fast asleep.

But there was no sleep for myself or my wife. We took turns keeping watch. At every groan of the ship's timbers, we feared that some change in position might sweep her away from the rocks. But they held her fast.

As the night passed, the sea grew calmer. And when the first faint light of dawn appeared, we saw blue sky above us. I awakened the boys and we all assembled on the remaining portion of the deck.

"Now," Ernest said cheerfully, "all that we have to do is build a raft that will take us ashore."

"I am afraid," I told him, "it would be impossible to make a raft that is safe to carry us. But let us look over the ship and try to find whatever will be of use."

Then all of us went off in different directions, and a short time later reassembled on the deck.

I had found extra stores of food and fresh water. Fritz had brought several guns, as well as powder and shot for them. Ernest produced a capful of nails and an assortment of hammers, chisels, axes and other tools. Little Franz carried a box full of fishhooks and several lengths of stout fishing line. He was also followed by two large dogs which he had found locked up in the captain's cabin, and they were eagerly showing their gratitude to him by leaping playfully around him and licking his face and hands.

"I have nothing to show," my wife said, smiling, "but I have good news. I found some animals still alive in the hold — a cow, a donkey, two goats, six sheep, a ram and a fine sow. I was just in time to save their lives by feeding them. There are also a number of chickens and geese in crates."

"Well done," I said, "but now we must find a safe way to get off this wreck and onto solid land once more."

During my search of the ship, I had seen a number of large casks floating in the flooded hold. The idea suddenly struck me that these could be made into a serviceable boat. The boys and I fished four of them out and dragged them up on deck. They were made of stout wood and strongly bound with iron hoops.

After hours of hard work, we succeeded in sawing each of them in two. Now we had eight big tubs ranged in a row. In the wreckage I found three long, thin planks. On one of them I nailed the eight tubs, and bent the two ends of the plank up to form a keel. We nailed the remaining two planks along the sides of the tubs and brought them to a point at each end.

In order to keep the boat safely balanced in the water, I constructed outriggers — in the manner of the sea canoes of the South Seas' natives — by fixing long poles across the bow and stern and fastening small empty brandy kegs to their ends. We now had a fine vessel that was steady and seaworthy.

By the time all this work had been completed, evening was drawing on. Since the storm had passed and the sea was calm, we decided to spend one more night on the ship. We had a hot supper, and then all retired and slept soundly and peacefully.

A Desolate Island

I T WAS with a great deal of difficulty that we got our awkward tub-boat over the side and into the water the next morning. But after much pulling and tugging, it was finally launched.

"Now," said I, "let us load as many supplies into it as we are able."

We quickly gathered a large quantity of ship's stores — canvas to make a tent, a chest of carpenter's tools, guns, pistols, powder, shot, fishing tackle, a large iron pot and several cases of food — and loaded them into the tubs.

"What about the animals?" my good wife asked anxiously. "Will it not be too far for them to swim?"

I puzzled about this problem for a moment, and then Fritz said, "Why not make swimming belts for them?"

"An excellent idea!" I exclaimed. And we set at once to work.

I caught one of the sheep and fastened a broad strip of canvas around its belly. To this I attached some small wooden kegs and empty tins. Then the boys and I pushed the frightened animal into the water. It sank, but in a moment it rose to the surface and struck out for the shore line.

In a short while we had made the same kind of cruae belts for the other animals, and soon all of our livestock were swimming bravely toward land. We placed the chickens in one of the tubs and covered it with wire netting. We released the geese, and they flew in to shore.

Now each of us got into a tub, little Franz sitting in the foremost one with his mother. The older boys and I took up our oars, and I shoved away from the side of the wreck. A strong tide was flowing shoreward, which carried us along with it.

When the two dogs, which we had named Turk and Juno, saw us leave the wreck, they jumped into the water and swam after us. We knew that they would not need safety belts like the other animals. Soon they were abreast of the boat, swimming strongly.

The nearer we approached to the shore, the less inviting it seemed. The barren rocks seemed to threaten us with hardship and misery. But by means of a telescope which I had taken from the captain's desk, I was able to distinguish green grass and tall palm trees beyond the cliffs.

The tide was carrying us toward the jagged rocks, but presently I saw an opening where a small stream flowed into the sea. I steered toward it, and soon we found ourselves in a small bay where the water was smooth and shallow, and which had a gently sloping beach.

All of our animals had made the shore safely, and we relieved them of their awkward swimming belts and allowed them to forage for themselves. We released the chickens and then began unloading our supplies.

We quickly erected the tent, and while the boys ran off to find moss and grass for our beds, I built a fireplace of large stones. Dry twigs and seaweed soon had a merry blaze going and I filled the iron pot with fresh water and placed it on the fire. Just as I was doing so, I heard Jack suddenly shout for help, as though in great danger.

I grabbed up a hatchet and ran toward the rocks of the beach. The little fellow stood in the shallow waters of a tidal pool, and I saw that an extremely large lobster had caught his foot in its powerful claw. Jack was in a terrible fright, kicking as hard as he could to dislodge the lobster, but it managed to hang on.

I quickly waded into the water, seized the lobster firmly by the back, and caused it to give up its hold. I held it up and laughed. "Using your foot as bait," I said, "you have managed to catch us all a delicious dinner."

I carried the lobster back to the camp and dropped it into the pot of boiling water. Meanwhile, Ernest had found a bed of oysters, and we feasted in royal style.

After we had eaten, and Fritz and I were busy storing the goods that we had brought from the wreck, Ernest went wandering off to the other side of the island. In an hour he was back, his face flushed with excitement.

"Father," he said, "I crossed the stream and went around to the other side of the rock cliffs. It is a beautiful country, so different from this, and the green grasslands run down to the beach in a gentle slope. Best of all, the beach is covered with all manner of casks and boxes that have washed in from the wreck. I think that we should go and collect it before the tide carries it out to sea again."

"You are entirely right, my son," I said. "We must allow nothing to go to waste that may be of use to us."

Accordingly, the three older boys and I, with Turk at our heels, set off for the place Ernest had discovered. Hundreds of crates, boxes and casks were floating in the water, along with fine beams, timbers and other lumber from the stricken ship.

We worked throughout the rest of the afternoon, tugging and hauling this treasure-trove out of the surf and onto the shore. Now the problem became one of how to transport these heavy materials back to our camp.

"We must make a cart, lads," I told them, "so that the cow or the donkey can be harnessed to pull it. But now it is beginning to grow dark, so we will put off this task until tomorrow."

Discoveries We Make

IMMEDIATELY after breakfast the next morning we went back to the beach where we had piled up the salvaged material. With the saw, I cut two cross sections from a tree that grew near the water's edge. Using these as wheels, we quickly put together a sturdy cart from the pieces of driftwood.

The evening before, lying by the fire after we had finished supper, I had contrived a crude harness of heavy sailcloth. With this we hitched our cow to the cart. We then piled the cart high with boxes and bales — and loaded as much on the donkey's back as it could carry — and set off to take it to camp. We dragged the lumber high up on the beach, so that it would be out of reach of the tides and ready at hand when we had need of it.

For several days we worked at salvaging everything that was floating in the water. Then, when the job was done, I decreed that we should all take a day of rest.

"May we take our rest by going on an exploring trip of our island?" Fritz begged.

I agreed that this was an excellent idea, and so Fritz and Ernest and I, followed by Turk, set off to see what we might see. The two younger boys and Juno stayed at our camp with my wife.

We had hoped to find some survivors from our ship, but although we walked for several miles along the beach, we saw no sign of men or boats. I could only conclude that they had been swept out to sea and so perished in the storm.

I grew sad when I realized the utter loneliness in which my little family now found itself. But I gave thanks that we were all safe and well, and resolved that we should make the best of our circumstances until some passing ship should happen by to rescue us.

This brief mood of sadness quickly passed, however, in the light of the discoveries we soon made.

Going through the thick vegetation that in places grew down to the edge of the water, we encountered a dense thicket of reeds. I feared that one of us might step on a poisonous snake, and so I cut one of the thickest of the reeds as a weapon.

I had carried it only a little way when I noticed a thick juice dripping from the end. Tasting it, I found that it was sweet and pleasant, and I knew at once that we were standing amidst a growth of sugar cane. Now we would never have to worry about sweetening for our food. Fritz cut some of the canes to take back to his mother.

A little farther along, Ernest, who had gone ahead, came running back toward us, holding up some vines with large roots in his hand.

"Father!" he shouted excitedly. "See what I have found! Potatoes!"

Fritz and I followed him and there, in a clearing among the trees, was a field covered by thousands of the precious plants.

"This is a wonderful discovery, lad," I told him. "As long as we have potatoes to eat, we will never be in danger of starvation."

Ernest gathered up a sackful of the vegetables to take back to his mother and we proceeded on our way. Suddenly Fritz pointed to a grove of trees that were of unusual appearance.

"Oh, what absurd-looking trees, Father! Look at those strange bumps on their trunks."

We approached to examine them, and I recognized them as calabash trees, the fruit of which grows in this curious way on their trunks. The fruit is also a species of gourd from whose hard rind spoons, cups and bowls can be made.

I explained this and then said:

"You see, boys, Nature provides man with everything he needs, if only he knows how to use it. Let us take a few of these gourds back to camp, and we will return later with the cart and gather a large supply — not only of these calabashes, but of potatoes and sugar cane as well."

It was now time for us to start back. Walking leisurely along, we came to a growth of coconut trees. The boys found a number of nuts on the ground, which they at once split open. But to their disgust they found that the meat was dry and uneatable.

"What's this?" cried Fritz. "I always thought a coconut was full of delicious sweet liquid."

"So it is," I told him, "when it is young and fresh. But as it ripens, the milk becomes congealed and in course of time is solidified into a kernel. The kernel then dries, as you see that these have done, but when the nut falls on favorable soil, the germ within the kernel swells until it breaks through the shell and then takes root and springs up as another tree."

We searched among the nuts that lay on the ground, but were unable to find one in which the kernel was not dried up.

"Nature makes sure that coconuts do not fall from the trees until they are overripe and ready to take root," I explained.

"Then how," Fritz asked, "are we ever going to get fresh ones? There are no limbs on the trunk and it is impossible to climb to the top where the nuts grow."

At that moment we heard a chattering in the palm fronds at the top of the tree.

"Look!" Fritz said. "Monkeys!"

Ernest laughed. "Now, my dear brother," he said, "I will answer your question for you."

He picked up a handful of pebbles and began to throw them at the monkeys. Their chattering increased, and then suddenly they defended themselves by pelting us in turn with coconuts. We rushed forward, picked up some of the finest of the nuts, pierced them, and drank the sweet cold milk. Ernest put a few of them in his knapsack, along with the canes and potatoes, and we continued on.

As we were leaving the coconut grove, Turk sprang away from us and rushed into a clump of high grass. There came a great squealing and chattering, and a troupe of monkeys that had been playing on the ground a little distance from the trees, scattered to the four winds as the big dog ran toward them.

Fritz went after him, and in a few minutes reappeared carrying a very tiny baby monkey in his arms. The little fellow was crying and whining, and clinging to Fritz's neck with its long skinny arms.

"He must have dropped from his mother's back when Turk frightened them so," Fritz said. "May we keep him as a pet?"

"I think he will be an amusing addition to our little group," I answered.

"Of course you may keep him."

In a few minutes, the little creature became calmer and climbed up on Fritz's shoulder. Then Fritz had an idea.

"Since you frightened his mother away, Mr. Turk," he said to the dog, "you will please carry the baby."

So saying, he placed the little monkey on Turk's back. The baby clutched the dog's collar with one tiny hand, and in a little while both animals seemed to enjoy this unique experience. And so, as we made our way homeward, the monkey rode along as proudly as any horseman trotting down a bridle path.

Everyone hastened to greet us as we approached our camp. Little Franz was particularly pleased with the monkey, and we agreed that it should be his pet. He immediately named it Master Knips, and the tiny animal at once climbed up on his shoulders and put its arms around his neck.

A bed of coals glowed in the fireplace. Two forked sticks had been planted in the ground on either side of it, and across them lay an iron rod on which were spitted half a dozen small fowl, slowly roasting.

"All this looks very tempting to a hungry traveler," I said to my wife, "but you should spare our poultry until the flock has increased."

"These are not our chickens," she laughed. "They are wild pigeons that Jack shot in the woods."

"There are thousands of them, Father," Jack said excitedly. "We shall never want for wild game."

"Then bury some of your potatoes in the coals and let them roast," I said to Ernest. "And we shall have a sumptuous meal indeed."

And sumptuous it was, for my good wife had found several barrels of Dutch cheeses among the supplies that had been washed ashore from the wreck. And so, when the birds and the potatoes were well-done, we sat down and did full justice to this appetizing food.

We Revisit
the Wreck

WHILE YOU were gone today," my good wife said as we all sat around the fire lazily after dinner, "Jack and Franz and I also did a bit of exploring. We found a large grove of the most enormous trees which I want you to see."

"Are they far from here?" I asked.

"No, only half a mile away."

I looked at the sun.

"There are two hours of daylight left. Will we have time to get there and back before dark?"

She said that we would, with time to spare.

"Then," said I, "I suggest that we go immediately to look at your wonderful trees."

We did so, and they were indeed the most unusual and magnificent trees

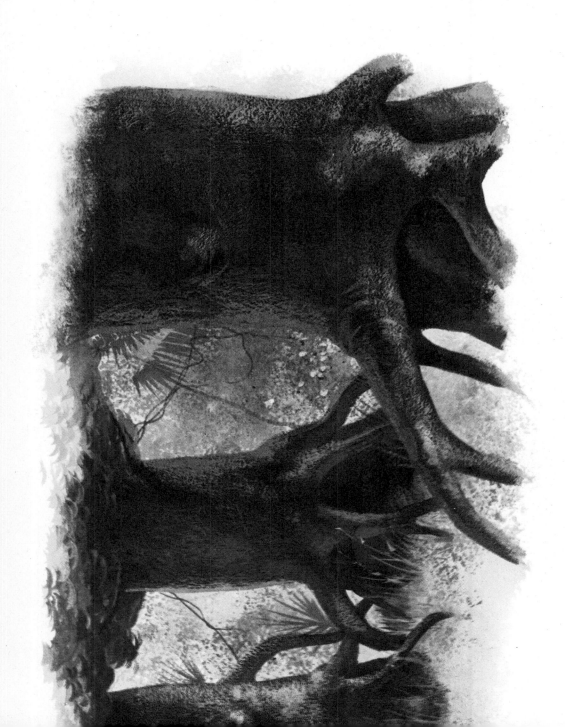

that I had ever seen. The massive trunks were more than fifty feet around, and they were supported by open-air roots that formed huge arches and props all around the trunk which was firmly rooted in the center. The foliage was thick and abundant and formed cool shade upon the ground beneath.

Fritz and Ernest were as amazed as I at these extraordinary trees which their mother had discovered.

"Do you have any idea in the world what kind of trees they could be?" Fritz asked.

"I have seen pictures of such trees," I replied, "and unless I am mistaken, they are the fig-bearing mangrove of the Antilles."

"When I first saw them this morning," said my wife, "it struck me that if we could build a house up in the branches of one of these noble trees, we would be perfectly safe and happy. No wild beasts could endanger us at night and we would be protected from storms and the wild waves of the sea."

"You have an excellent idea," I told her. "I agree that a fine tree-house would suit our needs perfectly."

The boys jumped up and down in their enthusiasm.

"Then may we start building it tomorrow, Father?"

I shook my head.

"Your mother mentioned the danger of storms. Another one, such as the one that shipwrecked us, might strike at any moment. When it does, it will surely break up the wreck and hurl it off the rocks, and all the valuable supplies that still remain aboard her will be lost. No, our first concern must be to retrieve everything of value that remains in the hulk of our poor ship. And after that is done, there will be time enough for us to build our tree-house."

At dawn the next morning, we started to make our plans for revisiting the wreck.

"I am afraid that our tub-boat will not be sufficient for carrying away all the heavy articles that we will find," I said, "so we must build a sturdy raft."

Leaving little Franz behind with his mother, the three older boys and I got into our tub-boat and soon made our way to the wreck that was still firmly held by the jagged rocks. Scrambling on deck, we began to look around. A number of large empty casks caught my eye. They seemed to be just what was needed for a foundation. We closed them tightly, pushed them overboard, and arranged twelve of them side by side in rows of three. These we firmly secured together by means of spars, and then laid down a substantial floor of planks. We constructed a low bulwark all around. When we were finished, we had a first-rate raft, exactly suited to our purpose.

Building the raft had taken the whole of one day. But I had told my wife that we intended to spend the night on the wreck, so that she would not worry about our absence.

The next day we set about loading the raft and boat. First we carried off the entire contents of our own cabins. Then we removed everything from the rooms of the captain and other officers, taking doors, window frames, bolts, bars and locks, as well as the furniture. We next took all the chests which contained clothing, tools, swords, knives and guns.

When the raft and the tub-boat were fully loaded, we rowed them into our little bay where we landed our cargo on the beach and at once went back for more.

It took us more than a week of hard work to remove everything from the wreck. One of the chests was filled with money, another with all manner of gold and silver watches, rings, bracelets and other jewelry. These were of no use to us on our desolate island, but I realized that they would make us rich if ever we were saved and taken back to civilization. And so we took them. More useful in our present circumstances was a case of knives, forks, spoons, plates, cups, dishes and cooking utensils.

The cargo of the ship on which we had sailed had been intended to supply a distant colony, and it proved a rich and almost inexhaustible treasure. To my delight, we found a number of young fruit trees, all carefully packed — apple, pear, chestnut, peach, plum and cherry. There were also sacks of corn,

In addition to all this wealth, we found iron-working tools, lead, paint, cart wheels, spades, axes and grindstones, as well as casks of butter, cheeses, hams, potted meats and sausages. One of the most important discoveries of all was several barrels of gunpowder and large quantities of muskets and pistols.

When we had stripped the wreck clean of everything that we could use, only one item remained.

Hunting through the hold, Fritz had found the separate parts of a small sailing sloop, with rigging and fittings complete. Now that salvage work was complete, the boys urged me to let them try to put it together. Such a fine little vessel would be a valuable addition to our store of possessions, for in it we could quickly sail to all the distant parts of our island. But assembling the craft would be quite a problem.

I finally hit upon a plan.

"Boys," I said, "what we need is room to work in. Bring axes and we will break down the compartment walls and clear out the space all around. Then we will have plenty of room for putting our sloop together."

"But after she is assembled," Ernest protested, "how will we get her out of this hold?"

"We will blow a hole in the side of the ship and float her out," I told him. I was not as confident as I made my voice sound, but this seemed to be the only possible chance we had of launching the little ship, and I was determined to take it.

The individual parts of the sloop were carefully arranged in order and each part marked with numbers. And so we set about the task of fitting them together. But it was a difficult job. It was several weeks, working all day every day, before it was done. We started to the wreck at dawn every morning and returned each evening just before dark descended.

At last, after incredible labor, all was completed. The sloop stood ready to be launched, but imprisoned within massive wooden walls.

"Now, lads," I said, "we will make our try."

I got a large cast-iron mortar, filled it with gunpowder, secured a block of oak to the top and through this I pierced a hole for the insertion of the fuse. I then placed the mortar in such a position that when it exploded, it would blow out the side of the ship. Finally, I lit a long fuse that would burn for some time, and the boys and I climbed into the tub-boat and rowed out to a safe distance.

I listened with strained nerves for the explosion. And then it came! A flash! A mighty roar! A grand burst of smoke and flame!

We quickly pulled for the wreck, and there a marvelous sight awaited us. The side of the ship had been completely torn out. The water was covered with floating wreckage. But there, inside the shattered hull, exposed to view and apparently unharmed, lay the little sloop. The boys cheered as they followed me into the blown-up hold.

It was little trouble to launch her. We stepped her mast, rigged her sails, and as the late afternoon sun glowed crimson in the west, Jack and Ernest sailed her proudly into our little cove. Fritz and I followed in the clumsy tub-boat.

I had left two barrels of gunpowder on board the wreck. Having stripped her of everything of value, I had determined to blow her up.

Early next morning, Fritz and I sailed out in the sloop. We attached a long fuse to the powder, lit it, and put back for shore. We had no more than landed when a vivid pillar of red fire rose from the water. A loud roar boomed across the sea. And the good ship that had carried us to this place from our old home in Switzerland was no more.

By evening the shore was lined with a rich store of planks and driftwood. During the next several days we stacked it in piles for future use.

The Tree-house

WE HAD NOW been on our island for several months, living all the while in our tent by the cove where we had first landed. Then one morning, on the day after we had finished storing everything from the wreck, I announced that it was time to begin the construction of the tree-house which was to be our permanent home.

My wife and the boys were overjoyed, for the tent at best provided crowded living quarters and they were anxious to get started on the building of a roomier, more comfortable dwelling.

From the cart wheels we had found in the wreck and the fine timbers that had washed ashore, we had made a large wagon which our cow and donkey could pull with ease. This we loaded with lumber and tools and set out for the grove of mangrove trees.

Arriving, we carefully examined the different trees and chose one which seemed best suited to our purpose. Heavy branches spread out at a great height above us.

"But how will you get the heavy beams up into the tree, Father?" little Franz asked.

"Just be patient," I said, "and I will show you."

Looking around, I selected a long, pliant sapling which I cut down and trimmed. I strung a stout piece of cord from end to end to make a bow. Then I found a long, straight reed which I shaped into an arrow.

"Now," I said to my wife, "can you supply me with a ball of light, strong thread?"

She procured one from the bag that she always carried. I fastened one end of the thread to my arrow and aimed at a large branch above me. The arrow flew upward, bore the thread over the branch, and fell at our feet. By means of the thread, I hauled a heavier rope up and over the limb.

While I was doing this, Franz had obtained two coils of rope, each about forty feet in length, which he stretched out side by side on the ground. He then cut thick canes of bamboo into two-foot lengths, and these we passed through knots that I had made in the ropes. Now we had a strong rope ladder, which I pulled up into the tree by means of the line that lay across the limb. We anchored the rope securely.

Now all of the boys were eager to be the first to climb the tree.

"Jack shall have the honor," I decided, "since he is the lightest. So up with you, my boy, and be careful."

Jack was as agile as a monkey, and he sprang up the ladder and quickly gained the top. Fritz was soon by his side, and with hammer and nails he fastened the ladder permanently to the tree.

I followed with an axe and carefully looked over the huge mangrove. It was ideally suited to our purpose. The branches were very strong and so closely interwoven that no beams would be required to form a flooring. When some of the boughs were lopped off and cleared away, a few planks would be quite sufficient.

I now called for a pulley, which Ernest tied to the cord hanging beside the ladder. I hauled it up and fastened it to a stout branch above me. Now we would be able to hoist up the timbers we needed to build our house.

We fell to work with our axes and chopped off all the useless boughs, leaving a few about six feet from the floor, from which we might sling our hammocks. We left others that were still higher to support a temporary roof of sailcloth.

Hauling up planks with the pulley, we arranged them side by side on the foundation of boughs to form a smooth, solid floor. Around this platform we built wooden walls on three sides, and then, throwing the sailcloth over the higher branches, we drew it down tight and firmly nailed it.

We had built only half a wall in front, so that the fresh sea breeze could blow directly in. We then hauled up our bedding and hammocks and hung them from the branches we had left.

And so, after only one day of hard work, our tree-house, though far from as finished as I intended it to be, was ready to be lived in.

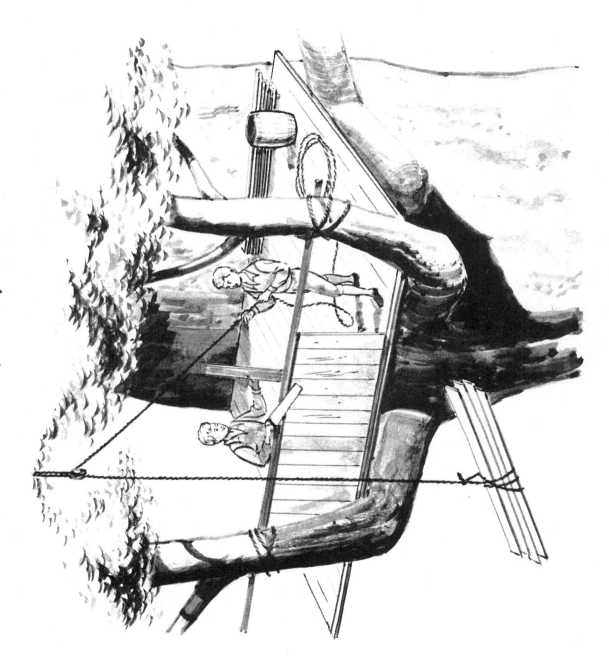

After supper, we ascended the rope-ladder to spend our first night aloft. The boys scampered up the ladder in a moment. But their mother, although the tree-house had been her idea, climbed up very slowly and cautiously. When she was safely within the house, I took little Franz on my back and followed.

I drew up the ladder behind me and then, with a greater sense of security than we had enjoyed since landing on the island, we all stood together in our new home.

"I do not believe," said my wife, "that I will ever become used to climbing up that flimsy ladder!"

"You will not have to for long," I promised her, "for while we were working today, I got an idea that will turn this nest into a wonderful castle in the sky."

Falconhurst

WHEN WE had climbed down from our perch the next morning and my wife was preparing breakfast, I decided to put my idea to the test.

"I think," said I to the boys, "that the trunk of this tree is partially hollow, for yesterday I noticed some birds flying in and out of a hole in its side. For all we know, it may be hollow for the greater part of its length."

"There is only one way to find out," said Fritz, and soon he and the other boys were climbing over the tree like so many squirrels, peering into the holes and tapping the wood to discover how far down the cavity extended. We thus determined that the trunk was hollow for most of the distance from the ground to the height of our house.

First, we cut an opening at ground level exactly the size of the door we had taken from the captain's cabin and which, hinges and all, was ready to be hung. Then we began the laborious task of clearing the rotten wood from the center of the trunk. This took us several days, and when the job was at last finished, the inside of the tree was like a great smooth tunnel.

It was now ready for the staircase. First, we erected in the center a stout sapling to form an axis round which to build the spiral stairs. In this, we cut notches to receive the steps, and corresponding notches in the tree itself to support the outer ends. The steps themselves we formed carefully and neatly of short lengths of planking and clenched them firmly in place with stout nails.

Upward and upward we built, cutting windows in the trunk as we required, to admit light and air, until we had raised our stairway from the ground to our tree-house. To make the ascent of the stairs perfectly easy, we ran a handrail on either side, one around the central pillar and the other following the curve of the trunk.

Then we fitted the door and the windows we had salvaged from the wreck, and at last we had a fine entryway to our new home.

After the stairway was completed, we set about enlarging the house itself. We built permanent walls and a roof of wood to replace the temporary one of sailcloth. We added two additional rooms, one as a bedroom for the boys and another as sleeping quarters for myself and my good wife. The original room that we had first built became our study and living room. We built shelves around the walls to hold the books that we had brought from the wreck, and furnished it with the ship's chairs and tables, as well as sundry pieces of furniture that the boys and I made in our spare time.

When the house was finally completed, Fritz said:

"This fine home of ours deserves a name. What shall we call it?"

"Since your mother was the one who found this charming place," I replied, "she must have the honor of naming it."

We all looked at her expectantly.

She thought for a moment, and then she said:

"Our home is as high as a hawk's nest. And so we shall call it 'Falconhurst.'"

And Falconhurst it became from that time on.

All of this work had taken us many months. And in between the various parts of the job, we found time for the other tasks that confronted us. Not far from Falconhurst, we found an admirable clearing in which we planted an orchard of fruit trees. Close by we plowed up a field for sowing our wheat and other grain. We prepared a huge garden for the beans, peas, corn and other vegetables, and soon we had a thriving farm.

Our cow had presented us with a fine bull calf. The sow had had a litter of pigs. The chickens and geese had multiplied fruitfully. And before long we found ourselves in possession of as fine a plantation and stock farm as any that could have been found in our native Switzerland, and a great deal better than most.

We called the plantation "Woodlands."

Thanksgiving

I HAD kept a careful journal of our activities every day since the shipwreck. And now I found, to my amazement, that we had been on the island for a full year. I read back over my notes and was astounded at the progress we had made.

Where first we had lived in a tent on the rocky shore, we now owned a fine tree-top home. Our farm was flourishing. Our flocks of animals were increasing. We had everything that we needed for living a comfortable life.

A few months before, while we were completing our house in the tree, Fritz had gone off on a hunting trip and captured a young buffalo that he had wounded with a shot from his gun. The beast soon became well, and as it did so it became tame. In no time at all, Fritz was riding it like a horse.

At about the same time, on another hunting venture, the boys had surprised a flock of ostriches and Ernest had succeeded in bringing home a young male bird. Like the buffalo, it quickly became tame and loitered about the clearing underneath Falconhurst as calmly as an overgrown chicken.

"Do you think, Father," Ernest asked, "that I could ever break Hurricane" —for so he had named the bird— "to the saddle? He runs as fast as the wind and I am sure he is strong enough to carry me."

It had never occurred to me that it would be possible to saddle and bridle a bird. But now I began to give the idea some serious thought.

I knew that most birds have one thing in common. At night, or when its eyes are covered, a bird is powerless. But when light returns, life and energy are restored to it. It is for this reason that a hunting falcon is quiet and docile when a hood is over its head, and why it is possible to pick a chicken off its perch in a darkened henhouse.

With these things in mind, I made a leather hood to be slipped over the ostrich's head. I cut holes in it for the eyes, and over these eyeholes I contrived square flaps or blinkers, which were arranged with fishbone springs so that they closed tightly of themselves. Reins were connected with these blinkers so that the flaps might be raised or allowed to close at the rider's pleasure.

When both blinkers were open, the ostrich would gallop straight ahead. Close its right eye, and it turned to the left. Close its left, and it turned to the right. Shut both, and it came to a stop and stood still.

I then made a small saddle, which I placed on the big bird's shoulders, as near to the neck as possible, and secured it with strong girths around the wings and across the breast.

In a very short while, Ernest had learned how to manage his mount. And soon all of us were riding gaily around our island — Fritz on his young buffalo, which he had named Storm, Ernest on Hurricane, Jack on the cow, Franz on our young bull calf, and I mounted astride our faithful donkey.

And so I decreed that on this first anniversary of our stay on the island we should celebrate Thanksgiving Day.

We started out with athletic contests among the boys. First we had a foot race, which Jack easily won. Then came a "horse race," but this was hardly a contest because Hurricane, the ostrich, was two or three times as fast as our poor four-footed beasts.

We then had a series of swimming and diving contests in the water offshore, and it was during one of these events that Ernest, who had swum out several hundred yards, came racing in at breakneck speed and ran up the beach to where his mother and I were sitting looking on.

"Father!" he panted as he ran. "Father! I have seen the most amazing sight! A giant clam — oh, it is as big around as two washtubs — has been washed in by the tide and is lying on the bottom of the bay! Is it possible, or were my eyes playing tricks with me?"

"No," said I, "the thing you saw is undoubtedly a *tridacna*, the giant clam of the tropic seas. And it is not safe to swim or dive while it is there, for these clams have been known to close their shells on the feet of unwary divers and drown them."

"Then let us capture it," the boys cried eagerly. And this we determined to do.

We sailed out in the sloop to the spot where Ernest had seen it, and looking down through the clear, green water we could plainly make it out as it lay on the white sand of the bottom. I knew that some of these giants weighed nearly a thousand pounds.

"How are we to capture it, if going near it is dangerous?" Fritz asked.

"I think I have an idea," I said.

I took a length of heavy rope, attached a lead weight to one end, and lowered it into the water. The *tridacna's* shell was open so that the sea water from which it fed might have free passage in and out. I let the weighted rope end into the opening, and the shell at once clamped tight over it.

"Now," I told the boys, "the clam will not let go as long as it has the rope in its shell. And so we can safely haul it up and drag it into shore."

This we did, and when we succeeded in making the clam open its shell by lighting a fire under it, we saw the great mass of pink meat inside which looked like the flesh of any clam of ordinary size.

"Is the giant clam good to eat?" my wife asked.

"As good as any other clam," I said, "and even more so. For the meat of this clam possibly weighs fifty pounds and will provide stock for more gallons of fine soup than we will care to eat."

When we had removed the meat, we washed the two halves of the shell clean with sea water. As Ernest had said, each was as large as a double washtub and both were lined with a glistening coating of mother-of-pearl.

"What lovely tubs they make!" little Franz cried.

"And just right," said I, "for a plan I have had in mind for some time. Each day your mother has to carry water from the stream in buckets for her household chores. So I now propose to install a plumbing system. And it seems to me that Thanksgiving Day is an excellent time to begin it."

The boys set to work with a will, but it was a full week before the project was completed. First we had to build a dam across the small river some distance upstream so that the water might be raised to a sufficient height to run down to Falconhurst. Then we made pipes from sections of large bamboo trees and carefully fitted them together. These allowed the water to flow into the two giant clamshells which we had placed on two stone platforms. One of these shell basins was used for washing, and the other as a reservoir for fresh drinking water.

And thus our life went on. Day after day brought its own work, and we had no time to idle or feel sorry about our separation from the world.

The Pearl Grotto

IT WAS toward the end of our second year on the island that I decided the entire family should have a vacation. We had harvested the crops from our flourishing farm and stored them, and I felt that everyone had earned a rest. And so we all got aboard the sloop, which had comfortable living quarters, and set sail around the island.

All of us had been so busy since the very day that we landed from the wreck that we had had little time for exploring. And this we now determined to do in a leisurely fashion.

The sea was calm and quiet as we sailed along the coast, past rocky cliffs, sandy, palm-lined beaches and heavy forests that often extended down to the water's edge. Thousands of sea birds sailed overhead, chattering and squawking as they flew. And on some of the rocks seals basked lazily in the warm sun.

At the end of the second day, we came to a high, rocky cape that extended far out to sea. Opposite us, in the side of this cliff, was a magnificent archway. Sailing through it, we found ourselves in a lovely landlocked bay.

The water beneath us was clear as crystal, and we saw beds of large oysters clinging to the rocks on the bottom.

"What a lovely place!" my wife exclaimed. "Let us stay here and enjoy it for a day or two."

"And I," said Fritz, "will dive down and bring up some of those fine-looking oysters for our supper."

In a few moments he had a large pile of the shellfish on the sloop's deck, and everyone set about the task of opening them. To his amazement, the first one that Fritz opened contained a large, lustrous pearl.

"Look, Father!" he cried excitedly. "These are pearl oysters!"

"We are rich, father!" Ernest said.

Each one of the oysters held a pearl in its shell. Some were large, some were small, but all were of perfect texture and proportion.

For two days the boys brought up the oysters, until at last we had a large chest filled to the brim with these jewels of the sea.

"In our present circumstances," I said, "these are as valueless as pebbles. But, like the money chest we took from the wreck, they will be a source of vast wealth should we ever again come into contact with the civilized world."

New Switzerland

THE YEARS went swiftly by. We enlarged Falconhurst, our tree home, and built another like it nearby in which the boys lived much of the time. We had planted flower gardens all about, with fountains shooting up lovely streams of water in the center.

Our flocks and herds of sheep and cattle supplied us with all the mutton, beef and veal that we could eat, and I had made a loom on which my good wife was able to weave fine woollen cloth to make our clothes. The orchards were thriving, as were our fields of vegetables and grain.

Fritz and Jack had built a watchtower on a point of land that jutted out into the sea and on this they had mounted one of the ship's cannon, ready to be fired in the event — which after all these years I deemed unlikely — that a vessel should happen by. A Swiss flag, which my wife had made, flew from a long pole at the tower's top as a signal.

Best of all, excellent health had been enjoyed by the entire family. The boys had grown into fine handsome fellows.

Fritz, now twenty-five, was of moderate height, uncommonly strong, active, muscular and high-spirited.

Ernest, two years younger, was tall and slight, and was the scholar of the family.

Jack, at twenty, strongly resembled Fritz, being about his height, though more lightly built.

Franz, a lively lad of seventeen, possessed some of the qualities of each of his brothers, in addition to a keen wit and a charm that was all his own.

Each member of the family had his duties to perform, and one of Jack's was to fire the sunset gun. Since we had retrieved an almost limitless supply of gunpowder from the ship, far more than we could ever use, we had adopted the custom of firing a salute each evening from the cannon on the watchtower.

One evening, by coincidence almost ten years to the day since we had been cast ashore from the wreck, we were all sitting on the beach enjoying the cool breeze when Jack fired the gun. To our utter amazement, he had scarcely done so when three answering shots boomed across the water from the sea.

We were speechless. Was it our imagination? Or had we really heard guns from a strange ship? Jack quickly loaded and fired again. And again the three shots responded from over the horizon.

"Did you hear them? Did you hear them?" the boys shouted, jumping up and down in their joy. "Now we will see our beloved country once more."

Night fell swiftly, and there was nothing to be done. But I instructed Jack to fire the gun at hourly intervals until morning.

None of us could sleep, and we were down at the beach again when the sun came up. To our utter astonishment, the first light of dawn showed a large ship, with the flag of England flapping at her masthead, sailing toward our bay. We all quickly jumped into the sloop and sailed out to meet her.

The sailors aboard lined the rails and stared at us incredulously as we cheered and waved at them. For of all the strange sights they least expected to see, we were it — a family cruising along in a pleasure yacht thousands of miles from the nearest civilized land.

The ship dropped anchor in the bay, and after circling her twice, we sailed up close and dropped our own. Fritz and I stepped into our dinghy and pulled for the ship. The captain welcomed us warmly and invited us to his cabin.

I briefly told him our story, and he explained what his vessel was doing in these waters.

"It is only by the most unusual of circumstances," he said, "that we happened to be within a hundred miles of this vicinity, for it is far off the regular shipping routes and indeed your island is not even on the charts. A week ago, we too were blown far off our course by a severe storm. And it was while we were trying to get our bearings that we heard your signal shot. It is well that you kept signaling throughout the night, or we might have missed you entirely."

The captain then insisted that my wife and the other boys be brought aboard, and accordingly dispatched a boat to fetch them.

We were royally entertained, and at luncheon we met the passengers — an invalid gentleman, Mr. Wolston, his wife and two daughters. A sea voyage had been recommended for Mr. Wolston's health, but it had not done him as much good as had been anticipated. The storm of the week before had shaken him up badly, and he longed for a few days on shore.

My wife accordingly invited him and his family to be our guests at Falconhurst for as long as the ship might remain in our harbor. He gladly accepted, and after the meal was finished, the captain and the Wolstons followed us in the ship's gig to our home.

The surprise of everyone turned to wonder as our party walked up the graveled path to Falconhurst — the huge, sprawling tree-house itself, the outdoor dining patio with its broad, shady balcony, the fountains in the flower gardens sparkling in the sun, the long rows of fruit trees heavy with their harvest.

They were even more amazed when my wife, with the help of the boys, laid the table for dinner. All of our best china and silver were brought out for the occasion. The table was covered with a spotless damask cloth. Wine from our grapes glowed in glass decanters. Pineapples, oranges, apples and pears rested on cool green leaves. A haunch of venison, hams, cold chicken and roast fish occupied the table's center.

In the evening, the captain returned to his ship. But Mr. Wolston and his family accepted our invitation to stay in our guest bungalow.

That night, my good wife and I had a long and serious discussion. Now that the opportunity presented itself, did we really want to return to Europe and abandon our lovely island home on which we had found so much happiness?

It soon became apparent that neither she nor I wished to leave, but only to spend the rest of our days here in the midst of the beauty and plenty we had created.

"But we will send the boys," she said, "and when they arrive back in Europe, they will endeavor to send out more emigrants to join us. And thus in time, we will form a prosperous colony."

"And in honor of our old home," I declared, "we shall call the colony New Switzerland!"

On the following morning, when we informed the boys of our plan, Ernest declared that he wished to go to Europe and there study medicine at a university. "For," he said, "as New Switzerland grows and prospers, it will need the services of a doctor."

We agreed that little Franz, too, should go back to school in Switzerland. Jack and Fritz both declared their intention of staying.

"Some day," said Fritz, "I would like to go back to our old home, just for a visit. But not now. In another month the crops will be ready for harvest."

Jack echoed this sentiment.

Mr. and Mrs. Wolston and their daughters also voiced a wish to remain with us, and Mr. Wolston said that he would send word for his son to come and join us. The Wolston girls were lovely and I had watched both Fritz and Jack casting shy glances in their direction. I thought it might not be too long before New Switzerland saw its first weddings.

After a week, the captain, having provisioned his ship from our stores and filled his casks with fresh water, declared that he was ready to set sail.

Everything was provided and packed up that would add to our boys' comfort on the long voyage. I also gave Ernest the chest of money which we had taken from the wreck — for it was ours by right of salvage — and the chests of pearls. I knew that he could sell these in the jewel markets of Europe for a fabulous fortune, and this money could be used for the future needs of our new colony.

The captain promised that our island would be duly given its rightful place upon the charts of the world, and that a ship would stop by at regular intervals, bringing emigrants and supplies.

And so on a fine morning, two days later, we said good-by to Franz and Ernest, and the great ship sailed out of our little bay on the ebb tide.

As it disappeared over the horizon, my wife grasped my arm and said softly:

"Good-by! Good-by forever to old Switzerland!"

And then Jack echoed the feelings of all of us.

"Hurrah for New Switzerland!" he shouted.